What Will the Weather Be Like Today?

Also illustrated by Kazuko
Cuckoobush Farm

Also by Paul Rogers
From Me to You

What Will the Weather Be Like Today?

PAUL ROGERS
PICTURES BY KAZUKO

Scholastic Inc.
New York   Toronto   London   Auckland   Sydney

Pour la famille Bony
P.R.

To my mother
From Kazuko

ISBN 0-590-45013-1

Text copyright © 1989 by Paul Rogers.
Illustrations copyright © 1989 by Kazuko.
All rights reserved. Published by Scholastic Inc.,
730 Broadway, New York, NY 10003,
by arrangement with Greenwillow Books,
a division of William Morrow & Company, Inc.

45 44 43 42   9/0
Printed in the U.S.A.   40
First Scholastic printing, September 1991

Just at the moment
when night becomes day,
when the stars in the sky
begin fading away,

you can hear all the birds
and the animals say,

"What will the weather be like today?"

Will it be windy?

Will it be warm?

Will there be snow?

Or a frost?

Or a storm?

"Be dry," says the lizard,
"and I won't complain."

The frog in the bog says,
"Perhaps it will rain."

The white cockatoo
likes it steamy and hot.

The mole doesn't know
if it's raining or not.

"Whatever the weather,
I work," says the bee.

"Wet," says the duck,
"is the weather for me."

"Weather? What's that?"

say the fish in the sea.

The world has awakened.
The day has begun,

and somewhere it's cloudy,

and somewhere there's sun,

and somewhere the sun
and the rain meet to play,

and paint a bright rainbow
to dress up the day!

How is the weather where *you* are today?